THE AVOCADO TREE

THE AVOCADO TREE

El Árbol de Aguacate

DIANE MYLOD

Authored by Diane Mylod, 2021

For my father who had to leave so suddenly and has found a way to let me know he is still here with me.

Para mi padre que se tuvo que ir pronto peró ha encontrado la manera de estar aquí conmigo

Right in the center of our front yard, you were planted.

~

Fuiste plantado en el mero centro del jardín de enfrente.

You were cared for and boasted about- just like he did with us (his children).
You felt the energy and love he was so good at spreading.

~

Te cuido y presumió como lo hacia con nosotros. Sentiste la energía y el amor que él era tan bueno en compartir.

6

He was patient with you, even though you made him wait...

~

Fue paciente contigo, aunque lo hiciste esperar...

He tied a red bow around you because he believed it would *"cast away envious eyes."*
I thought it made you look more beautiful.

~

Te amarro un listón rojo para que no te hicieran *mal de ojo.* Yo pensaba que te hacia ver mas hermoso.

You grew so unbelievably tall until one day...You gave avocados!

~

Creciste tan grande hasta que un día...¡nos diste aguacates!

Everyone came to see if it was true. In Arizona? How?

~

Todos vinieron a ver si era cierto. ¿ Arizona? ¿Como?

You required a lot of work.

~

Necesitabas mucho trabajo.

Your Avocados were shared with many- and we all continued to feel the positive energy as well as the
love he was so good at spreading.

~

Tus aguacates fueron compartidos con muchos- Y todos seguíamos sintiendo su energía y el amor que era tan bueno en compartir.

The day came when he no longer could take care of you. He was gone and we were all grieving the loss of his energy and love.

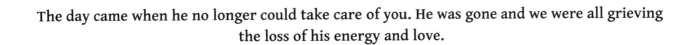

Llego el dia en el que ya no pudo cuidarte. Se tuvo que ir y todos extrañamos su energía y amor.

You stopped giving avocados. We wondered when you would give avocados again.

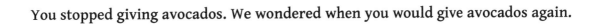

Dejaste de dar aguacates. Nos preguntamos cuando darías aguacates otra vez.

Time went by until one day... You shared your energy and love once again and gave us avocados!

~

El tiempo pasó hasta que un dia.... compartiste tu energía y amor y nos diste aguacates otra vez!

You gave me the light I needed and I took one of your avocado pits and
began to grow an avocado tree of my own.

~

Me diste la luz que necesitaba para tomar uno de tus aguacates y plantar su semilla.

The pit from your tree grew so unbelievably fast for me. I now feel the satisfaction of what he must have felt.

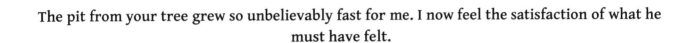

Tu semilla ha crecido increiblemente rapido para mi. Ahora siento la satisfacción que él sintió.

You are here with me and we will always continue to feel the energy and love you were so good at spreading.

~

Estás aquí conmigo y siempre sentiremos la energía y el amor que fuiste tan bueno en compartir.

REMEMBRANCE ~ REMEMBRANZA

"A society grows great when old men plant trees whose shade they know they shall never sit in."
-Greek Proverb

NICOMEDES RODRIGUEZ
(1945- 2016)

A Father, Husband, Grandfather, Farmer and Friend
Padre, Esposo, Abuelo, Granjero y Amigo

Autora y Artista

About the Author:

DIANE MYLOD, BA is a Mother, Wife, Educator, Author, Elementary School Teacher living in Phoenix Arizona with her husband, two boys and potted avocado tree. When Diane graduated from Arizona State University she became a teacher at the school she attended as a little girl in Glendale, AZ --and taught there for 6 years. Her husband often calls her the "Lebron James" of her career for taking her talents back to her hometown. There she became the gifted strand teacher for 5 years and then took on the challenge to teach English to students who were refugees from Syria, Mexico and Iraq in 2016. Diane is currently teaching Spanish to Second graders at a Dual Language Academy in the community she now lives in. Diane continues to explore her creative writing and expression inspired by life's different seasons and times of grief by creating a children's book to help other's in bereavement. Diane hopes to share her creative expression and love with the greater community of both Spanish and English speakers through her first published children's book, *The Avocado Tree,* also known as *El Árbol de Aguacate.*

About the Illustrator:

MORIAII MYLOD- DAGGETT, MΛΛT, ATR, RYT is a Visual Artist, Registered Art Psychotherapist, Body Somatic Yoga Teacher, Multidisciplinary Educator and an Adjunct Professor of Art Therapy residing in North-West region of New Jersey with her husband and two fur creatures. She primarily works in her home studio, *Birdseye in The Attic* where she explores various creative mediums- primarily painting applications on canvas, paper and wood. Moriah has been collaborating with fellow Creatives and working in the local community providing private group and individual art psychotherapy sessions with wide-range of populations and mentoring young artists. Moriah has experience in clinical work, expressive art lessons, trauma-informed presentations, poetry readings, creative arts workshops, community art projects such as murals, facilitating art experiential, yoga and guided-meditations. Moriah passionately pursued a Master of Arts in Art Therapy from Cedar Crest College in May 2016 and graduated from Cedar Crest College in 2013 with a B.A. in Art Therapy and a Minor in Art History-- where she was a recipient for the Howard Agar Memorial Prize for demonstration of significant ability in the studio arts.

COPYRIGHT

About the Author and Illustrator:

Diane and Moriah met when they were 15 years old. They shared a history class together and were surviving those high school years teenagers soon put behind them. It was a high school where being Hispanic-- mostly Mexican, was the majority. Diane was, Diane Rodriguez then-- and had no idea Moriah had a twin brother who would steal her heart in the most romantic way possible. That did not happen until months after knowing Moriah. Moriah was building on her love for art and shared her writing, art and acts of kindness with those around her. Moriah and Diane did not know they would spend the rest of their lives together or even work on a book like this together. They have now been in each other lives for 20 years.

CPSIA information can be obtained
at www.ICGtesting.com
Printed in the USA
LVHW071312011121
702124LV00004B/7